# Stress Relief

RECOVERY
DISCOVERY

# STRESS RELIEF

## *Overcoming Exhaustion, Relapse, and Burnout*

*Randy Reynolds & David Lynn*

ZondervanPublishingHouse
*Grand Rapids, Michigan*
*A Division of* HarperCollins*Publishers*

Stress Relief


Requests for information should be addressed to:
Zondervan Publishing House
Grand Rapids, Michigan 49530

ISBN 0-310-57311-4



*Edited by Linda Vanderzalm*
*Cover design by Lecy Design*
*Cover photo by Dan Hummel*
*Interior design by Ann Cherryman*

*Printed in the United States of America*

92 93 94 95 96 97 / DP / 10 9 8 7 6 5 4 3 2 1

# *CONTENTS*

*This book is dedicated to Jim Olson, who has taught me not only how to enjoy life and God but also how to play.*

*Randy Reynolds*

# *Introduction*

*Stress recovery?* you may be thinking. *I can understand recovery from alcoholism or recovery from shattering life experiences, but recovery from stress? Isn't stress just a reality that we need to live with?*

Yes. And no. Yes, we all experience stress. Yes, stress is here to stay. But that doesn't mean we accept it as a permanent resident in our lives. Stress is often destructive; it sometimes kills. We don't need to be a victim of stress's corrosive work on our bodies, minds, and spirits. We can protect ourselves.

Maybe you already are a victim of stress. Maybe you have stress-related physical problems: headaches, ulcers, heart problems, sleep problems, to name a few. Maybe stress has invaded your emotional stability and you experience anxiety or panic disorders; you may be controlled by anger, yelling at your spouse or venting your frustration on your kids. Or stress may have driven you back into old compulsions: you work too much or you go on cleaning binges or drink and eat too much or compulsively indulge in sex.

If you see yourself in any of these descriptions, we have good news: *you can recover from the negative effects of stress.* This workbook will help you discover the areas in which stress has a destructive effect. But beyond that, it will give you direction for reversing stress's negative effect and maintaining a more healthy balance in your life. The primary help will come from the Old Testament principle of sabbath—a God-ordained time to cease from labor and be refreshed and renewed in body, soul, and spirit.

Each chapter in this workbook consists of five sections. *Recovery Focus* highlights the issues the chapter will discuss. *Recovery Information* explains the effects of stress and the remedies of the sabbath principles, while the *Recovery Probers* gives questions that help you take a personal look at your stresses and areas that need change. The *Recovery Guide* is designed to help you explore Scripture passages that help you integrate the sabbath principles into your life. At the end of each chapter, the *Recovery Goals* gives you a chance to formulate goals that you need to work on as you move toward balance and recovery.

Take the time to write out your answers to the questions in each chapter. Reflect carefully on your feelings and beliefs. Pray, asking God to use this workbook as a tool for your recovery. Then discuss your insights and feelings with someone—ideally with a small group that will study this workbook together.

If you are part of such a group, speak up. Share your thoughts with the group. Look to the others for help and support. Learn from them as they share their stories and struggles. Pray together, depending on God to work in your life. And rejoice together as you grow and find wholeness.

If you aren't able to be part of a small group, talk over your insights with a trusted pastor, counselor, or balanced friend. Share your responses and questions with that other person. Ask him or her to pray for you regularly.

# 1. Worn-out and Weary

## RECOVERY FOCUS

- Identify situations that contribute to your weariness.
- Recognize the symptoms of stress.
- Examine the consequences of stress in your life.

## RECOVERY INFORMATION

"I'm tired, depressed, and out of control. Other than that—everything is okay," Alice said with a wry smile on her face.

Alice was on a treadmill. She worked two jobs, feeling that was the only way she and her husband could get out of debt. However, when she worked seventy hours a week, she would get exhausted and become irritable, demanding, needy, anxious, and sick. To cope with this stress, she would overeat and shop compulsively, which only made her feel worse about herself. She became desperate to escape this destructive cycle, but she felt trapped. "I can't seem to relax, and eating is one of the few things that seems to relieve the irritability and anxiety. If I keep eating, though, I'm going to have to buy a new car because I'm outgrowing the one I'm in."

Although Alice tried to joke about her problem, she was in pain. She felt very little enjoyment or meaning in her life, and she didn't know the first thing about how to relax and be refreshed in healthy or godly ways. She was a driven woman, and she couldn't stop.

People get worn-out from many different kinds of situations. Check which of the following situations describe you:

- ☐ Significant or multiple losses (like death, separation, children moving out of the house, loss of relationships through conflict or a move, illness)
- ☐ Tasks you feel inadequate to do (like parenting, certain aspects of your job, managing your time, fulfilling people's expectations of you)

- ☐ Excessive demands (like caring for aging parents who have moved in, caring for several young children, special job projects, living with needy people)
- ☐ Constant threats (like the threats of losing your job, divorce, illness, injury, death, violence from an abusive spouse)
- ☐ Feeling trapped in a situation where you feel you can't win (like situations at your job, in your marriage, in a child-parent conflict, illness)
- ☐ Chronic pain in a physical or emotional area (like illness, codependency, lost relationships)
- ☐ A surprise trauma (like death, loss of a job, news of an illness, injury, learning of a spouse's infidelity)
- ☐ A significant change in your life (like moving, marrying, divorcing, giving birth to a child, having a child leave home, losing a job or taking a new one)
- ☐ Significant events (like getting a promotion at work, having a baby, having a child graduate or get married, going on a trip)

Scott, forty-one, was exhausted. Although he was a successful businessman, active father, and community leader, Scott was often depressed. He felt as if there wasn't enough of anything to go around: not enough money, not enough time, not enough energy, not enough Scott.

Scott couldn't understand why he felt the way he did. His wife loved him; his kids loved him; his boss and co-workers respected him. Even though he liked his life, he also felt guilty and anxious much of the time. He began having trouble getting to sleep and an even harder time staying asleep. At times he was so irritable and tense that his children complained to his wife about it. He began catching colds, flu, and other infections. And he had a difficult time concentrating at work and staying motivated. Often he would fantasize about what it would be like to escape his responsibilities.

When Scott came for counseling, he began to realize that underlying all of his feelings was a sense of pressure, stress, and exhaustion. Maybe you recognize yourself in Scott's situation. Read the following list of symptoms and check those that describe you.

- ☐ Apathy
- ☐ Tension
- ☐ Insomnia
- ☐ Headaches
- ☐ Nail biting
- ☐ Feeling used
- ☐ Loss of appetite
- ☐ Nervous laughter
- ☐ Neck or back pain
- ☐ Intestinal distress
- ☐ Loss of concentration
- ☐ Loss of interest in sex
- ☐ Feeling overwhelmed and overextended
- ☐ Feeling irritable, frustrated, or easily angered
- ☐ Increased use or desire for alcohol, food, tobacco, sugar, or sex

List additional symptoms that describe you.

- 
- 
- 
- 

People who do not pay attention to their symptoms can pay a high price. As Karl, forty-five years old, advanced up the corporate ladder, he found he often worked long hours and even overlooked vacation time in order to meet deadlines. He began to experience some physical problems, but he ignored them, even though his wife communicated her concern for his health.

A week after Christmas, Karl landed in the hospital and stayed there for several months. He had developed a serious lung condition that would become a chronic health problem. He had also ignored his family history of heart disease and had his first heart attack. Karl had ruined his health, and with it he also lost his job. As Karl reflected on his life, he said, "I know God was telling me to slow down, but I ignored his voice." He expressed regret, recounting how he had been driven by fears of losing his position. He knew he had not trusted God with his life.

What are the consequences of not taking care of yourself and ignoring the warning signs of an exhausted body and mind? Is it really godly to push yourself over your limits, even for good purposes?

Doctors tell us of a definite correlation between stress and disease, both mental and physical. In the article "Stress on the Job," *Newsweek* reported that stress produces absenteeism and medical costs to the tune of $150 billion a year (April 25, 1988, p. 40).

The relationship between stress and disease is not new. During the time Pasteur discovered bacteria as a disease agent, a scientist named Bernard wrote that in order for the body to be infected, it had to be in a state that it could receive pathogenic microbes. Stress or "dis-ease" can produce that state. Disease from stress occurs when the person's adaptive system overloads and breaks down because it can't keep up with change, demands, and adjustments.

There are many ways people pay the price for not taking care of themselves. Karl paid a high price for ignoring the symptoms that were screaming at him to slow down. He lost his physical health. Scott was losing his emotional health by becoming depressed. Alice was relapsing into compulsive behaviors by not facing her fatigue head on.

What about you? Do you listen to your body and your emotions when they warn you that something is wrong? Is this part of your Christian responsibility, to pay attention to the "dis-ease" in your life and do something that puts you more at peace?

## RECOVERY PROBERS

1. **In what areas of your life do you feel the most pressures and demands?**

2. **What is the most draining area of your life?**

3. **What consistently pushes you past your limits?**

**4. Which exhaustion symptoms worry you the most?**

**5. What concerns do you have if your life doesn't change? What concerns does your family have?**

**6. How can loving something be a detriment to your life?**

**7. What destructive behavior patterns do you lapse into when you are exhausted?**

**8. How serious is your exhaustion? Are you at the burnout point? How would you know if you were?**

## RECOVERY GUIDE

Does God care about your health? Does it matter to him if you take care of yourself? A look at some Old Testament names of God gives us a clue. God is called *Jehovah,* which means "the existing one," and *Jehovah Jireh,* which means "God will provide," and *Jehovah Shalom,* which means "God is peace." If God will provide for you, how does that encourage you to take care of yourself? How does that demonstrate that God is concerned about your health? If God is peace, then what does that mean for your feelings of exhaustion and burnout?

**Read 1 Corinthians 3:16–17.**

1. What does God think about your body?

2. What is Paul's message in this passage?

3. How seriously does God take abuse of his temple?

4. How may you be destroying God's temple?

5. How can you treat your body as "sacred"?

**Read Matthew 11:28–30.**

1. Is it Jesus' desire to have you overburdened?

2. How can Jesus lighten your load?

3. What would rest do for you?

4. **How does your soul rest?**

## RECOVERY GOALS

1. **What rituals or activities help you recuperate when you are tired and weary?**

2. **How often do you do them?**

3. **What keeps you from doing them?**

4. **What can you build into your life to ensure more rest for your weary body, mind, and soul?**

5. **What other changes do you need to make in order to take care of yourself?**

6. **When will you begin?**

# 2. The Stages of Burnout

## RECOVERY FOCUS

- Identify your level of burnout.
- Submit your stress to God and find serenity.
- Determine how you can work toward health.

## RECOVERY INFORMATION

What is a healthy life? When God brings renewal into our lives, what does it look like?

A healthy life includes vitality and enjoyment. The color has not been washed out, leaving a drab, routine experience. A healthy life includes stimulation, creativity, harmony, and balance.

Life is not supposed to be all work and battle, but it can easily fall into that experience as responsibilities become routine. When was the last time you watched a child in awe and realized that you've lost your sense of wonder? When was the last time you discovered something new and fresh and felt energized by that discovery? When was the last time the color of a sunset engulfed you or you caught yourself enraptured by a field of flowers? When was the last time a bird's song interrupted your train of thought and lifted your spirits? When was the last time you smelled your spouse's hair or wrestled with your children on the living room floor?

Have your worries, responsibilities, and battles squeezed the joy and pleasure of God's goodness out of your life? How does life drain from you when you become exhausted, worn-out, and weary?

The stages of deterioration in health can be progressive in their levels of intensity. The more exhausted or stressed you feel, the more recovery is needed to bring you back to health.

George came to counseling because he was suffering from panic attacks. He would become overwhelmed by waves of anxiety and feel weak and afraid that he was going to have a heart attack and die. He had showed signs of exhaustion for several years as he had worked long hours building a new business. He had been constantly irritable and short-tempered with his wife.

About a year after establishing his business, George faced two heavy stresses: his wife had an affair and competition threatened his business profits. George began to have a sense of dread about work and life in general. George became agoraphobic—he was afraid of everything—and his fear crippled him. His body chemistry was out of balance, and the slightest threat would throw him into panic and make him feel out of control.

George went to his medical doctor and was put on medication that helped the panic disorder. George had been in a severe state of exhaustion. It took almost a year of counseling for him to be able to learn to relax and enjoy life again.

Are you like George, severely exhausted? Are you on the road to that point? Let's look at four stages of health deterioration from exhaustion and stress to help you understand at what level you may be functioning now.*

**Stage one.** If you are in stage one, you may be irritable and easily frustrated. You may lose some of your motivation and lapse into doing things because you should rather than because you want to. You may begin to feel tired and worn-out by tasks that energized you before. The rut you feel you are in may seem as if it is getting deeper. A sense of being used or taken advantage of may bring feelings of resentment and grumbling. This stage may be characterized by a loss of serenity that is more than periodic.

**Stage two.** In stage two, the level of intensity increases. You may have the feeling that you have lost freedom and that your life is controlled by outside forces. Instead of feeling merely irritable or angry, you have become bitter and can't seem to release your anger. Your anxiety increases, and you may show signs of depression: loss of sleep, change in eating habits, lack of concentration, restlessness, nail biting, desire to isolate. You may show signs of physical distress, such as headaches, backaches, neckaches, or intestinal problems. This stage can be characterized by escape fantasies and a feeling of being trapped.

**Stage three.** In stage three, the level of intensity increases even more. The longer you stay in stressful situations, the more the symptoms increase. You may experience depression with thoughts of

*The first three stages can be found in the book *Compassion Fatigue* by Randy Reynolds (Serendipity House, 1990).

suicide or wishing that others would die. Your bitterness turns to hatred and vindictive thoughts. Your physical problems may intensify to include heart disease, immune-system problems, or intestinal problems, like ulcers or irritable bowel. You may find you isolate yourself from people and demanding situations. You may find yourself involved in compulsive behavior patterns: eating or drinking too much, working unreasonably long hours, becoming overly religious, cleaning obsessively, indulging in compulsive sexual activity. This stage is characterized by desperation, pain, or depression.

**Stage four.** In stage four, the exhaustion leads to a total breakdown in one of the above-mentioned systems. If you are in stage four, you are in danger of having heart attacks and becoming incapacitated. You may break down emotionally, overwhelmed by a depression or anxiety that is beyond your ability to handle. You may have panic attacks and be in constant fear of all sorts of situations: riding on planes, getting into elevators, or mixing with groups of people. In this stage the phobias (fears) become debilitating. Your compulsive behavior may be totally out of control, causing problems in your ability to function. Stage four is characterized by a physical, emotional, or spiritual breakdown. As in stage three, the symptoms need immediate attention from qualified people such as doctors, pastors, counselors, or the staff of treatment centers.

What do you do when life becomes unmanageable because of stress, exhaustion, and change? Many of us continue to do the same things we are already doing, only we try harder. This is Alcoholics Anonymous's definition of insanity—doing the same things over and over again, expecting different results. We become driven over potential losses with no rest stops along the way. We get our motivation from fear and insecurity and push ourselves without mercy or reflection. It is our rigidity and inflexibility that keeps us from recovery and vitality.

We may act and feel as if God doesn't exist, or if he does, that he doesn't care. We may feel that it is up to us to make life work the way it should. This causes us to feel powerless, anxious, and angry at times, as if our lives are out of our control.

But feeling powerless is not bad. Although our instincts tell us to avoid all situations that leave us feeling powerless, the truth is this: *admitting that you are powerless is often the first step to change*. People in a twelve-step recovery program know that admitting that their lives are out of control and unmanageable is the foundational first step. And the first step leads to the second: God can restore us to wholeness.

Reinhold Niebuhr, a Protestant theologian, saw that people need God, not themselves, as their main frame of reference. This would allow them to be more tolerant of life's uncertainties and more flexible with change. Out of Niebuhr's belief came the Serenity Prayer:

> God, grant me the serenity
> to accept the things I cannot change,
> the courage to change the things I can,
> and the wisdom to know the difference.
>
> Living one day at a time;
> enjoying one moment at a time;
> accepting hardship as a pathway to peace;
> taking, as Jesus did, this sinful world
> as it is, not as I would have it;
> trusting that you will make all things right
> if I surrender to your will;
> so that I may be reasonably happy in this life
> and supremely happy with you forever in the next.

Staying healthy means making the goals described by this prayer a priority in your life and believing that God will grant you these qualities. Serenity, courage, acceptance, enjoyment, trust, and surrender to God all restore health. It is not enough for you to recognize the craziness in your life: you must surrender your life—as unmanageable as it is—to God.

David Lynn, in his work with recovering alcoholics and addicts, has found this surrender to be a pivotal point of recovery. Once those suffering from addictions were able to turn their lives over to God, they began to experience some serenity in their lives.

## RECOVERY PROBERS

**1. In what ways are you healthy?**

**2. In what ways are you not healthy?**

**3. Do you find it difficult to have intimacy and rest in your life? Explain.**

**4. What physical problems do you have (headaches, grinding teeth, diarrhea, rashes, muscle spasms, colds, and flus)?**

**5. What emotional problems do you have (depression, anxiety, angry outbursts, loss of concentration, apathy)?**

**6. What social problems do you have (isolation from others, alienation and feelings of alienation from others, acting inappropriately and breaking rules, people complaining about you or withdrawing from you)?**

**7. What addiction or compulsion problems do you have (the overuse of substances such as drugs or alcohol, overeating, overexercising, use of tobacco to ease tension, buying things you can't afford)?**

**8. In what stage of exhaustion are you? What symptoms of this stage most concern you?**

**9. Are you getting help for the burnout you are experiencing? From whom? Is the help effective?**

10. Do you feel you have permission or freedom to make changes that would give you relief, or are you trapped? How?

## RECOVERY GUIDE

Read John 10:10.

1. What does God want for you?

2. The Greek word for "life" is *zöe,* which means "life intensive." What does it mean that God wants to give you life intensive?

3. Who or what are the "thieves" in your life?

4. How are they trying to destroy you?

5. Are you willing to seek God from your heart to find an answer to your stress-related health problems or burnout?

Read Romans 14:17.

1. Is joy a part of your experience in God's kingdom? How do you lose your joy?

2. Is peace a part of your experience in God's kingdom? How do you lose your peace?

## Read Philippians 4:4–9.

1. List the directives given in verses 4–6.

☐

☐

☐

☐

☐

☐

2. Mark with a + the attitude or behavior that is already part of your life. Mark with a – the attitude or behavior that is not part of your life.

3. God does not say that your life will be easy or without cost and difficulty. In fact, he promises that in "this life you will have trouble" (John 16:33). How can you look for good things in difficult situations and find acceptance (vv. 8–9)?

## Read James 1:2–4.

1. Does it say that trials (stresses) are fun and that you will feel great when they come? What should your attitude be in times of stress?

2. Why does this seemingly foolish advice make sense?

**3. What are the good things that come from trials (stresses)?**

## RECOVERY GOALS

**1. Evaluate the presence of each of the healthy characteristics in your life. Mark an S in front of those that are strongly present in your life; mark a W for those that are weak or not present in your life.**

- ☐ Sobriety
- ☐ Enjoyment
- ☐ Creativity
- ☐ Contentment
- ☐ Productivity
- ☐ Sense of humor
- ☐ Love for others
- ☐ Tolerance of change
- ☐ Positive self-esteem
- ☐ Sense of hopefulness
- ☐ Courage or risk taking
- ☐ Control by God's spirit
- ☐ Ability to relax and rest
- ☐ Peace of mind or serenity
- ☐ Purpose or mission in life
- ☐ Ability to be close to others
- ☐ Sense of safety or God's protection
- ☐ Responsiveness to God, life, and others
- ☐ Ability to protect yourself
- ☐ Acceptance and being able to see good in difficulty

**2. What are your weakest areas?**

**3. What are your strongest areas?**

**4. How will you work on your weak areas?**

**5. Whom will you enlist to help you?**

**6. What people in your life model the areas in which you are weak? How can you learn from them?**

**7. Is staying healthy a priority in your life? What do you do to stay healthy?**

**8. What changes are you willing to make to improve your health and encourage recovery from being exhausted?**

# 3. Getting the Support You Need

## RECOVERY FOCUS

- Recognize your need for support and love.
- Find ways to gain meaningful support.
- Allow God's unconditional love to give you security and meaning.

## RECOVERY INFORMATION

The latter stages of exhaustion often come when you feel that what you are doing is not important to others or yourself. When you feel life is neither rewarding nor meaningful, it feels as if you are caught on a treadmill, going nowhere.

Studies show that when people find warmth and support during stressful times, the negative impact on their body and its system is reduced. Renewal often starts when you find that someone, somewhere cares.

Norman Cousins spent ten years studying and interviewing people at UCLA, looking for correlations between attitude and healing. He said, "There was abundant medical research to show that the brain under circumstances of negative emotions—hate, fear, panic, rage, despair, depression, exasperation, frustration—could produce powerful changes in the body's chemistry; even set the stage for intensified illness." However, there was not much evidence to show that positive emotions such as purpose, determination, love, hope, faith, will to live, and festivity, would be helpful in the healing process. So he set out to find studies and cases where this proved to be a factor.

Immunologist Ronald Glaser and psychologist Kiecolt-Glaser did one such study with caregivers of Alzheimer's disease victims. The study indicated that caregivers who were involved in a support group saw their immune systems enhanced and their emotional health increased. These caregivers felt less lonely in their lives. The fellowship made a difference.

In Randy Reynolds's early years as a pastor, he struggled with burnout. He worked two jobs to support his family. One year his work became very strained. It seemed that the congregation didn't appreciate his leadership and made what Randy felt were unreasonable demands. Randy began to question the value of his work. Was ministry worth it?

A few months later, Randy went on a pilgrimage to a Christian conference, looking for God to speak his love and affirmation. Feeling empty and abandoned by God and others, he caught the flu but managed to attend several talks, one of them by Ray Stedman, a pastor Randy had always deeply respected. He had not seen or spoken to Dr. Stedman for years and did not know him well.

Randy sat through one of Dr. Stedman's talks, already knowing what he would say next because Randy had read his books and listened to his tapes. After the talk, Randy still felt forgotten by God and empty inside. He walked to the front of the room to say hello to Dr. Stedman, who was surrounded by a large crowd of people.

However, as Randy approached, Dr. Stedman looked over the crowd, saw him, and yelled out, "Randy! Randy Reynolds!"

Randy was so deeply moved by Stedman's recognition that he could hardly speak. It was as if God himself had spoken from heaven saying, "This is my son in whom I am well pleased." The turning point in Randy's struggles to minister in his congregation was the knowledge that God himself cared about his struggles. He had found the support he needed.

Support groups are flourishing in America with an estimated 1.5 million meetings per week. Why? Simply put, we need to have others know us and care about us. We need a place where we can share our struggles and release anger and fear and receive validation and hope.

Without regular support, many stressed people revert to compulsive behavior or find they relapse into unhealthy patterns. Stress can make people more self-centered and demanding, feeling no one understands them. One couple who had become alienated from their church community had experienced years of chronic physical pain. This did not help their dispositions and made it hard for others to stay close to them. They would tell people who came to visit them, "No one really cares for us." This seemed totally irrational to the visitors because here they were, in the couple's home, trying to show them that they cared.

Frustrated with the couple's behavior, their pastor wondered if they were demon possessed. At times they met his best efforts with rejection and anger. He enlisted the help of a Christian counselor, who referred the couple to a chronic-pain support group. The couple responded positively to the group and began to make progress. They soon reestablished relationships at church and with their families.

God created us with the need to belong to something larger than ourselves. In community we find the security and strength we need to overcome stress. Studies show that one of the main factors helping prisoners of war survive was the prisoners' ability to connect with others. And the Bible calls the individual Christian to be a part of the body of Christ.

Often, when overwhelmed and stressed-out people go to meetings where they can hear how others are overcoming struggles, they become more relaxed and tranquil. They no longer feel alone in their difficulty. Connecting with other people is essential to help us relax and feel more secure.

A fifty-four-year-old executive who made over $60,000 a year was laid off. "I was overwhelmed with a sense of restlessness and hopelessness," he said. He joined a support group of other executives who were going through a similar experience and found hope and peace in the group.

What are your needs for support? Have you found places and experiences to meet those needs? If you've tried to go it alone, reconsider your presuppositions. Recognize that you need the input and support of other people. If you find it hard to locate support, to find the people who can identify with your situation, look for church and community groups that offer support. You can identify these by asking a pastor or Christian counselor for a referral. Or call a local information and referral service for more information.

## RECOVERY PROBERS

**1. With what group(s) of people are you connected?**

**2. Do you feel understood in this group? Are you real in the group?**

**3. How does the group bring a sense of security or relaxation to your life?**

**4. How does the group give you hope in your struggles? Is the group alive for you?**

**5. With whom do you share your negative emotions? With whom do you feel safe to share your life, your innermost thoughts?**

**6. Do you tend to withdraw from others or draw close to others when you are under stress? Do you withdraw or draw close to God?**

**7. What is the most rewarding thing you do?**

**8. What helps you relax and feel secure in your life?**

**9. Is it difficult for you to know what you are feeling when you are exhausted or stressed?**

**10. Do you turn to compulsive behavior before you talk to others or go to support groups?**

## RECOVERY GUIDE

When you feel as if no one cares for you, remember that the Bible says God loves you, and his love is unconditional and always available.

When a well-known theologian was asked what he thought was the most profound message of the Scriptures, he said, "Jesus loves me this I know, for the Bible tells me so."

**Read Romans 5:8.**

1. **How would you respond to someone who was willing to sacrifice his only son so you could live?**

2. **How does this expression of God's love for you give you peace?**

**Read Romans 8:35–39.**

1. **Have you felt cut off from God's love? What do you feel separated you from God's love?**

2. **What does this passage communicate to you?**

3. **How do you feel knowing that God's love is always available to you and that nothing can separate you from it?**

**Read 1 John 3:16–18.**

1. **How does this passage show love to be more than a passive thought?**

2. When others satisfy your needs, how do they feel?

Read Acts 2:44–47.

1. What does a Christian community offer to those involved?

2. When people care for one another and give to each other, how do they feel toward God and each other?

Read 1 Corinthians 12:14–27.

1. What does it mean to you to know you are part of the body of Christ?

2. How have you acted as if you don't need other parts of the body?

3. What part of the body of Christ can help you right now? How will you put yourself in a position to receive that help?

## RECOVERY GOALS

1. When you feel stressed, is it healthier for you to withdraw or to find support from a community of understanding people? Explain.

2. **How does connecting with other people help you relax and feel secure?**

3. **To whom do you feel safe talking? If you don't have a friend or group from whom you can gain support, what will you do to find one?**

4. **List the people who may be able to relate to your present situation.**

5. **List any group or groups that would be a support to you.**

6. **When will you get involved in this group (if you're not already)?**

7. **What keeps you from making a connection with others? Commit that to God and take a risk to get involved in a wise way.**

# 4. The Sabbath Principle and Stress

## RECOVERY FOCUS

- Understand your arousal-activation-recovery cycle.
- Understand the importance of the sabbath principle.
- Integrate the sabbath principle into your life.

## RECOVERY INFORMATION

When you are under stress, your body automatically undergoes some physiological changes to prepare you to cope with the stress. Some people call this the fight-flight response. We choose to describe it as an arousal-activation cycle. Let us explain what we mean.

When you are under any kind of stress, your body pumps adrenaline into your system, producing more energy to confront what is making demands on you or threatening you. This *arousal* reaction releases a variety of chemicals: cortisol and cortisone fight inflammation, increase muscle tension, and expand blood sugar; adrenaline and noradrenaline activate the heart muscle, send blood sugar to the muscles, and raise blood pressure. All this produces arousal and prepares you for some dispersal of energy.

*Activation* is the next stage, where you use that energy. You may use your energy on meeting a deadline or dealing with extra family demands. Somewhere, you need to disperse this energy physically. If you do not have a physical outlet for the energy your body has produced, you may find all that energy will activate your mind with many thoughts and worries that can cause a loss of sleep.

The third stage is *recovery,* a time of rest or recuperating after activation. Figure 1 illustrates the completed cycle: arousal-activation-recovery.

Although our bodies automatically go into the arousal period, they do not automatically go into recovery. We must give our bodies, minds, and spirits time to rest so that they reach a point of equilibrium before they begin another arousal-activation cycle. Without this recovery time, our bodies will be damaged.

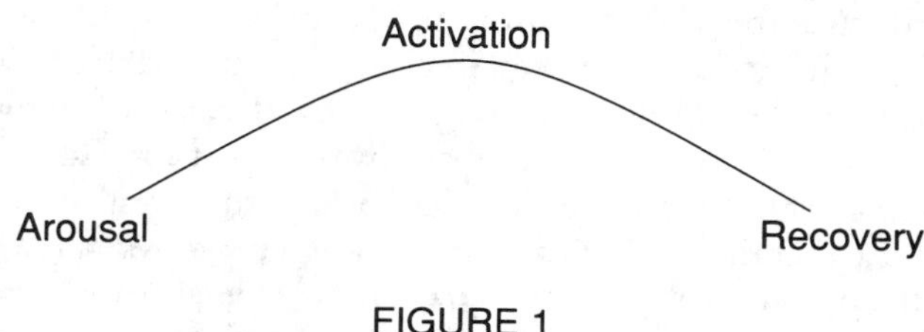


FIGURE 1

The constant arousal-activation reaction, with its accompanying physiological expressions, makes us feel alive and powerful, but without a rest, it can break us down. Some people become addicted to or dependent on this arousal-activation reaction and keep feeding it. Others wish they could just turn off the reaction.

People who have moved to the fourth stage of burnout and have panic attacks feel overwhelmed by the adrenaline flushes and get more flushes because of their fears. When the recovery time is shortened or eliminated, a person may eventually experience some negative consequences. People who are really exhausted feel tired constantly but are continually experiencing arousal and activation without the recovery aspect (see Figure 2).

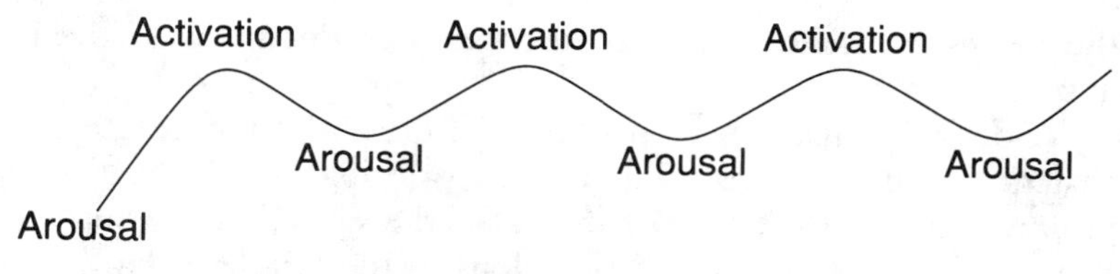


FIGURE 2

## THE SABBATH PRINCIPLE

Coming down off this arousal-activation cycle is what the sabbath is all about. It is structuring into our lives the rest, restoration, and recovery that rejuvenate us.

God instituted the sabbath as a time to cease from labor and be refreshed and renewed—in body, soul, and spirit. The Old Testament describes many sabbaths. The weekly seventh day of rest is the most familiar, of course, but God also provided for sabbaths that lasted from several days to a year.

God takes the sabbath seriously. He made it part of his creation dynamic. The Scriptures make it clear that the sabbath was very important for the Israelites. It was an integral part of having a right relationship with God. The sabbath was a part of God's plan in establishing a kind of rhythm to life. In Scripture, rest was based on the premise that the God of the sabbath was a protector and a provider for his people and that they could trust him. The sabbaths were to be a time of focus, when people could stop their work and worry and enjoy life because of their trust in who God is.

The consequences for not celebrating a sabbath can be costly. The arousal-activation-recovery cycle is like breathing, taking in a breath and giving out a breath—both of which are essential for the process to work. Right now, take in a breath of air and hold it. Now take in a little more and hold it. Take in still more and hold it. Do you feel as if you are about to burst? Now, exhale and feel yourself relax.

Driven people have only half the equation in their lives. They can be active, but they have a difficult time relaxing and receiving. The rhythm of an active and then passive but responsive side to life is absent. Driven people find life out of balance; they work hard, fight hassles, and are continually drained. They overlook the importance of the sabbath side of life, where a person relaxes, receives, enjoys, and is filled up. Often they feel they do not really have permission to let themselves experience a sabbath, since being productive and active is so important in adult life.

God gives us permission not to be driven by the demands and anxieties of life by providing us this principle of a sabbath. God promised the Israelites that if they kept the sabbath, he would bless them. This may have seemed ridiculous to the Israelites. How could they be more successful if they worked less and trusted God?

Working harder and longer may not be smart or even helpful. Forgetting God and his sabbath rest can be very harmful. In David Lynn's work with recovering alcoholics and addicts, he teaches a popular and simple strategy for avoiding relapse. It is called the HALT method: Don't get too

**H**ungry,

Angry,

Lonely, or

Tired.

Any one of these, and especially all four, symptoms contribute to relapse, making you more vulnerable to the urges and cravings to drink or use drugs. Following the principles of the sabbath helps you avoid the dangers of stress.

The next five chapters in this workbook will examine five components of the sabbath principle:

Disengaging

Finding Safety

Celebration

Quiet Reflection

Hope and Restoration

In these chapters we will look at how disengaging from the normal routine, finding safety, celebrating in the community, taking time to reflect, forgive, and worship, and choosing to hope in difficult situations can make a difference in your life.

## RECOVERY PROBERS

1. **How long does it take you to get your mind off your worries and relax in the normal course of a day?**

2. **Which chart, Figure 1 or 2, best illustrates your life? Why?**

3. **What kinds of sabbaths do you practice in your life routine?**

4. **Why do you think most people do not take sabbaths?**

**5. Do your arousal-activation reactions scare you?**

**6. Do you thrive on your arousal-activation reaction? Do you use any stimulants to keep the arousal going (coffee, tobacco, tea, sugar, diet pills, amphetamines, or other stimulants)? Explain.**

**7. Do you get depressed or feel guilty when you relax?**

## RECOVERY GUIDE

The Old Testament concept of the Sabbath had become a law and a burden to the nation of Israel by the time Jesus started his ministry. Jesus made it clear that the Sabbath was intended to be a benefit, not a burden, to God's people. The Sabbath was to be more of an atmosphere in a person's life rather than just a ritual. It was to give a person peace, rest, and restoration rather than more difficulty. The Sabbath in the New Testament meant rest for the soul as well as for the body.

### Read Matthew 12:1–14.

**1. What point was Jesus trying to make to the Pharisees about the Sabbath?**

**2. How do people overlook the purpose and spirit of the Sabbath and make it into something legal and compulsive? Do you?**

3. Was the Pharisees' rigidity over not working on the Sabbath good? Why?

4. When you think of the sabbaths, do you see them as meaningless religious rituals or something of benefit and blessing to you?

Read Hebrews 4:9–11.

1. What is your understanding of the Sabbath-rest described in this passage?

2. Have you entered that Sabbath-rest? How can you make an effort to enter that rest?

3. Israel did not enter into God's rest because they did not have faith or trust in God's promises and therefore missed God's blessing. How do your strivings overlook God's faithfulness to you? How do you miss God's rest in your life?

4. How does trust in God give you rest in your soul?

## RECOVERY GOALS

1. List again the kinds of sabbaths you practice in your life routine.

2. Rest for your mind and soul comes from trusting in God's faithfulness. Describe an experience when God has demonstrated his provision or protection in your life.

3. Write down a passage that helps you remember God's faithfulness to you.

4. Take in a deep breath and let it out slowly. Feel yourself let go of the tension in your body. Do this several times and while you do, think about the experience you wrote down. Think about the passage and what it says to you. Concentrate on relaxing your breathing. Close your eyes, ask God to take care of your concerns, and let go of them as you breathe. Practice this for five minutes a day for one week and then use it every time you feel tense.

# 5. The Sabbath Principle of Disengaging

## RECOVERY FOCUS

- Understand the importance of disengaging.
- Learn to disengage in refreshing ways.
- Trust God's provision for you.

## RECOVERY INFORMATION

Travelers on the Alaskan highway report seeing a sign that said, "Pick your rut carefully. You will be in it for the next thousand miles." Our lives can become much like that, stuck in a rut, unable to get out.

Do you feel that way? Is it hard for you to break out of your ruts, to back off from your involvements? One of the helpful aspects of the sabbath principle is learning to *disengage* from our routine, from our work, from our worries, from our responsibilities.

To be able to cease from labor and be refreshed and renewed is to cease from *all* labor—physical, emotional, and mental. Even when some people are absent physically from work, they are often there emotionally or mentally.

Unfortunately, in Protestant Christianity we have a well-developed theology of work, but not one for rest and play. Thus the concept of disengaging from our work is difficult to understand and practice. We feel guilty. We feel disloyal to God. We feel confused. So we stay engaged in our work.

We often feel that everything is dependent on us. We actually believe that if we worry enough about a situation, it will get better, and if we don't worry, life will fall apart. This belief reinforces a dependency on our own efforts: We find that when we work, we see results, and when we don't work, things don't get accomplished. Work becomes the center of the universe, and we worship and depend on it.

That doesn't mean work is not an essential part of our lives. Work is important, and we spend a large percentage of our lives doing it. However, *we are not meant to live to work.* It is wonderful to enjoy work and the benefits of work in our lives, but we are much more than our status or our possessions. We can take work or ministry too seriously and make it more important than God would make it or than it actually is.

Because work fills so much of our basic need for security and significance, we are afraid to disengage from our work. We feel that we are defined by what we do. If we disengage from our work, we feel as if we are doing nothing and we therefore are "nothing." When we begin to believe that we control and shape our lives, leaving out God's providence, we become slaves to work and its benefits.

We have a difficult time admitting that ultimately only God can control the results of our efforts. His blessing is what really produces a sense of significance and security in our lives, not our efforts or even the results of those efforts. Disengaging from our routine allows us the freedom to enjoy our work and not be controlled by it.

Many people confuse disengaging with escape. Escape is like junk food: it meets a need but doesn't have any nutritional value. Some things people use to escape are not only non-beneficial but also harmful, like drugs, alcohol, compulsive sex, or other compulsions or addictions that destroy a person's body and soul. Some of these activities give the illusion of rest, but they don't refresh and renew a person. The person ends up needing additional escape and has less courage to face challenges. Usually the more intense or painful a person's life is, the greater the need for intensity in the area of escape.

People in our culture often turn to television to relax and get their mind off their struggles. Although television may provide a distraction, it doesn't provide nourishing rest or inspiration. People are no more renewed after they watch a comedy, sporting event, or movie than they were before they sat down to turn on the television. Television is a passive medium that does not engage us in renewal. It may leave us empty or more stressed out than before.

## HEALTHY DISENGAGING

So how can we disengage in ways that renew us? One of the foundational ways of answering that question can be found in asking how God wants us to spend our time. God created us for a purpose, but that purpose was not, first of all, to work. "The chief end of man," says the Westminster Catechism, "is to glorify God and enjoy him forever." The sabbath reminds us that we can slow down and enjoy life and God.

In Psalm 16:11, David talks about enjoying God and the pleasures God has for us: "You have made known to me the path of life; you will fill me with joy in your presence, with eternal pleasures at your right hand." As we become caught up in the daily grind of stress, grief, demands, overstimulation, or whatever, we need to disengage and enjoy. Sometimes that means doing something different and slowing down our pace.

Tim Hansel begins his book *When I Relax I Feel Guilty* with this poem by Rev. Wilfred A. Peterson:

> Slow me down, Lord.
> Ease the pounding of my heart
> by the quieting of my mind.
> Steady my hurried pace with a vision
> of the eternal reach of time.
> Give me, amid the confusion of the day,
> the calmness of the everlasting hills.
> Break the tensions of my nerves
> and muscles with the soothing music of
> the singing streams that live in my memory.
> Teach me the art of taking minute vacations—
> of slowing down to look at a flower,
> to chat with a friend, to pat a dog,
> to smile at a child, to read a few lines from a good book.
>
> Slow me down, Lord, and inspire me to send my roots
> deep into the soil of life's enduring values,
> that I may grow toward my greater destiny.
> Remind me each day that
> the race is not always to the swift;
> that there is more to life than increasing its speed.
> Let me look upward to the towering oak
> and know that it grew great and strong
> because it grew slowly and well.

Disengaging gives us breaks from our routines so we can recharge our souls. Disengaging can help us to see and enjoy the good things in our lives and not take them for granted. Questions in the Recovery Probers and Recovery Goals sections will help you determine healthy ways you can disengage.

## RECOVERY PROBERS

**1. Has work become more important to you than God or enjoying life?**

2. **What causes you to depend more on your work and yourself than on God?**

3. **Make a list of activities that help you disengage but may be harmful (overeating, overspending, using drugs or alcohol to escape, overworking).**

4. **Make a list of activities that help you disengage but don't necessarily give you rest, inspiration, or renewal (watching television, playing a game, taking a coffee break, going shopping).**

5. **Make a list of activities that disengage you and give you rest and renewal (reflecting on good things while taking a walk, talking to a friend, reading Scripture, enjoying nature, reading an inspiring story, listening to music, reflecting on your relationship to God).**

6. **What are the sources of pressure on you when you try to relax?**

7. How selfish do you feel when you take time and space for yourself to relax and disengage?

8. The things we commit ourselves to often take over our lives and control us. What things in your life have too much control over you (work, status, material possessions, relationships)?

9. Do you feel that everything in your life depends on you? Whom will you let down if you do not continue at your present pace?

10. Are you taking on responsibilities that are really God's? What are they?

## RECOVERY GUIDE

Read Exodus 16:16–30.

1. What was God trying to do with his provision of manna?

2. What responsibility did the Israelites have with the manna so they could keep the Sabbath?

**3. What does this say about God's desires for his people to keep the Sabbath?**

**4. How has God provided for your Sabbath rest?**

**5. What types of things do you have to be responsible for in order to have a sabbath rest in your life?**

**6. In what area is it difficult for you to trust in God's provision?**

**Read Philippians 4:19.**

**1. Should you feel you are all alone in the struggles of life?**

**2. How do you feel when you know someone will take care of you?**

**3. According to this verse, how will God provide?**

**Read Philippians 4:12–13.**

1. **Does Paul's contentment come from everything being the way he wants it? How are Paul's contentment and serenity not dependent on his circumstances?**

2. **What does Paul draw from God?**

3. **Do you draw more inner strength from God than from your circumstances? How?**

## RECOVERY GOALS

1. **When you need to disengage, do you need to disengage from physical work, mental work, emotional work, or spiritual work?**

2. **What disengaging activities would you like to build into your life?**

3. **What steps will you take to make that happen?**

**4. People have found that these activities refresh them and help them recharge:**

- Meditate on Scripture passages daily
- Read a good book
- Take a walk and look for beauty
- Go to a concert
- Participate in regular worship activities
- Visit an art museum
- Sing with a choral group or with your favorite tape
- Take a nap
- Quit working while you still have energy to do something else
- Do breathing exercises after work
- Give yourself something to look forward to daily and do it
- Try something you've never done before
- Call a friend and talk about something enjoyable
- Spend time in a relaxing hobby

**5. Which of these activities will help you disengage? When will you begin to do these things?**

# 6. The Sabbath Principle of Finding Safety

## RECOVERY FOCUS

- Find safety and rest in God.
- Find safety in community.
- Break the anger and anxiety arousal-activation cycle.

## RECOVERY INFORMATION

The Old Testament sabbath was a time to worship God, the Provider God, the Protector God. This worship created a sense of safety for the people. They could focus once again on God's goodness and protecting love, helping them relax and gain perspective.

They saw God as their refuge, their shield, their rock, and their fortress. In Psalm 27, David internalizes these images, believes them, feels them, experiences them as he worships God. He says, "The Lord is my light and my salvation—whom shall I fear? The Lord is the stronghold of my life—of whom shall I be afraid? . . . For in the day of trouble he will keep me safe in his dwelling; he will hide me in the shelter of his tabernacle and set me high upon a rock" (Ps. 27:1, 5). It was not that David's life was free from trouble, threat, or hardship, but that David found refuge in the Lord for his soul.

That same sense of safety is available to you. You can find that sense of innocence and trust, allowing you to enjoy life even in the face of threat. The Lord can be a safe place for you. He wants to offer you refuge for your weary soul.

When Randy Reynolds and his family were flying home from a summer vacation, they found themselves in the middle of a violent storm. The plane began to be tossed around like a ping-pong ball in a washing machine. The passengers were warned to stay seated. The plane suddenly began to drop like a rock for what seemed forever.

People screamed, grabbed their seats, and hung on helplessly. As the plane began to gain altitude again, a stillness and tension that expressed group panic filled the cabin.

Out of this silence came the voice of an innocent child who was looking out of the window at the lightning, "Look at the pretty lights, Mama; look at all the pretty lights." The little girl felt safe and relaxed, while the rest of the passengers were paralyzed by fear. God can and will give us a sense of safety as we press into him even in the face of real threat.

## FIND SERENITY

One of the main by-products of the sabbath principle is serenity—undisturbed quiet or calm. In contrast to this are the people who too often find themselves constantly disturbed inside with anger, fear, or both. They find themselves on an arousal roller coaster.

Sue experiences this often. She may be driving along in her car and someone pulls out in front of her. An internal alarm goes off, and she emotionally reacts and becomes anxious. She starts thinking anxious thoughts and feels anxious feelings. This in turn sets off her arousal reaction and pumps adrenaline into her system. Sue interprets this as fear, which frightens her more and increases her anxious thoughts and feelings. Her hands get sweaty, and she says to herself, "It's too dangerous out here."

This cycle has to be broken to gain serenity. Either the physical arousal reaction or the negative thoughts and feelings need to be interrupted.

The arousal-activation-recovery curve can have either ***anger*** or ***fear*** as the main emotion of the arousal-activation reaction (as shown in Figure 3 and Figure 4).

To get off this negative arousal cycle, you need to make serenity a goal in your life. You must have a time of rest, a time that allows you to feel God's protection, even when you are working through difficult circumstances. This involves finding a safe place where you can't be aroused into fear or anger, where you can find rest for your soul, where you can put your reactions to rest. For some people, this is a physical place, like a mountain stream; for others it is prayer. For still others it is being with people who love them.

George was finishing his last year at seminary when tragedy struck. He was driving home from school one afternoon when a four-year-old boy ran out in front of his car. His car struck and killed the boy. George was traumatized by this experience and couldn't find any

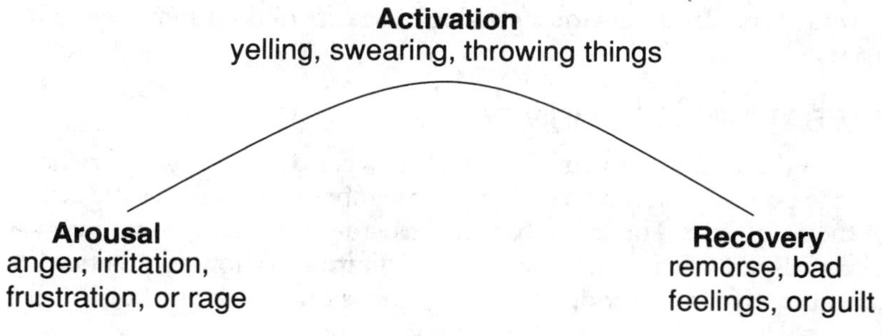


FIGURE 3

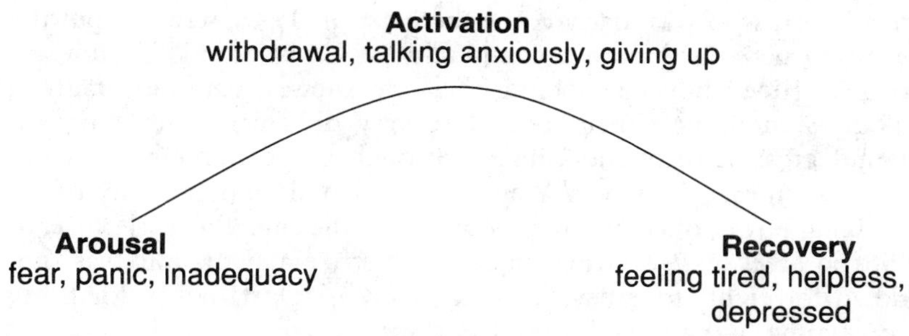


FIGURE 4

peace for himself. Whenever he drove down a street and saw a child, his heart would start racing. He felt responsible and afraid. He couldn't shake the trauma.

One day as George was reading the Bible, he found a passage he felt was written for him. In the Old Testament, God had provided cities of refuge for those who had accidentally killed someone. These were places that a person could go for safety after the accident. George felt that God was saying he knew that accidents are a part of life and that God would provide for and protect those who were victimized by them. This began to bring peace and relief to George as God became a refuge to him. Whenever George took time to think about these cities of refuge and dwell on God's goodness, he experienced some rest in his heart.

## SABBATH IN COMMUNITY

In the Old Testament the sabbaths were community experiences. All the people took time to rest and remember that God was the center of their universe. The sabbaths were structured so that community was a central part of the celebration. The definition of how to practice the sabbaths placed the individual, both physically and psychologically, close to his or her family and friends.

In our culture, where people are often lonely and isolated, we have a great need for community. Community brings a sense of security because it takes us beyond ourselves. Our anxiety is often reduced when we spend time with relaxed and stable people.

In his book *Life Together* Dietrich Bonhoeffer, a German theologian who was martyred by the Nazis in 1945, wrote about the strength he gained from a community of Christians. This group of people gained hope by sharing their weaknesses, pain, and faith in God. Even though their lives were very difficult, these Christians found great security and courage through this community of faith.

In *Stronger Than Steel* Wayne Alderson tells another story of the enabling power of community. Wayne was the chief financial officer at Pittron Steel in 1972 when there was a strike and the mill was shut down for eighty-four days. The company had lost money for thirty consecutive months and would not survive without a change.

When Wayne was promoted to vice president in charge of operations, he initiated a new management style that was less combative and more focused on developing a team between management and labor. Wayne made some of the first steps toward developing community in the workplace by spending time with the labor force, learning the names of all three hundred employees. Through his efforts, the mill became a place of encouragement.

Alderson had been challenged as a Christian to bring his values to the marketplace and test them there. He demonstrated God's respect for people by valuing each employee, no matter what that person did. He tried to reflect God's forgiving love in his relationships with his fellow workers.

The sense of community Alderson built had positive effects on the people and the company: sales went up 400 percent; profits rose to 30 percent; employment went up 300 percent; productivity rose 64 percent; labor grievances declined from as many as twelve per week to one per year; chronic absenteeism virtually disappeared; and quality of the product became the best in the history of the plant. The financial outlook improved from a six-million-dollar deficit to a six-million-dollar profit in less than two years!

God created us with a need to be connected to something larger than ourselves. We need God, our families, our friends, and our neighbors. With this connection comes meaning and loss of isolation and loneliness, leading us to safety and protection for our souls. Researchers at the University of California at Berkeley found in a nine-year study that "those who were single, had few friends or relatives, and shunned community organizations had more than twice the mortality rate of others."

## RECOVERY PROBERS

**1. Where did you find safety as a child?**

**2. Who protected you when you were a child?**

**3. How do you gain a sense of God's protection in your life now?**

- Prayer
- Meditation in Scripture
- Praise and worship
- Time outside with God's creation
- Readings stories of God's faithfulness
- Corporate worship
- Hearing other people tell of God's faithfulness to them
- 
- 
- 
- 

**4. When you get caught on the arousal roller coaster, which emotion tends to dominate your experiences, anger or fear?**

**5. Does finding a safe place and being able to relax mean that God will not allow anything difficult to come into your life?**

**6. What are you now doing to practice the community element of the sabbath in your life?**

**7. Are you willing to pay a price to belong to a community? What is most difficult for you in making a connection with God or others (time, energy, insecurity, resentment, trust, feelings of alienation)?**

## RECOVERY GUIDE

The Old Testament psalms powerfully articulate the writers' sense of aloneness and desperation as well as their trust in God's protection. When you feel vulnerable and unprotected, meditate on the psalms, placing yourself in the place of the writers. Say the words aloud, drawing strength and serenity from them.

### Read Psalm 84:10–12.

**1. Why does the psalmist value God's presence?**

**2. What are the good things he is looking for from God?**

**3. Do you desire to be close to God, to live in his presence?**

**4. What good things are you expecting in your relationship with God?**

**Read Psalm 91.**

**1. Where does the believer find rest?**

**2. List three verses that talk about threat.**

**3. List several areas in your life where you feel threatened.**

**4. What promises of protection does God make to you in this psalm?**

**5. Internalize this psalm by listing ways in which God protects, delivers, and helps you.**

**6. Read this psalm several times a day for a week and study what it says to you every time you read it. Say it aloud, changing the pronouns so that the psalm becomes a personal prayer of faith:**

> I will say of you, "You are my refuge and my fortress,
> my God in whom I trust."
> Surely you will save me from [whatever threatens you]
> and from [whatever disturbs your serenity].
> You will cover me with your feathers,
> and under your wings I will find refuge.

**Read Psalm 133:1.**

**1. What safe and harmonious relationships do you have?**

Find strength and safety in verses from these psalms as well. Memorize verses that are especially meaningful to you in your situation right now. Internalize the words of these psalms so that they become part of your daily thought processes.

| | | |
|---|---|---|
| Psalm 27 | Psalm 46 | Psalm 91 |
| Psalm 34 | Psalm 57 | Psalm 121 |
| Psalm 37 | Psalm 71 | Psalm 136 |

# RECOVERY GOALS

## FEEL GOD'S PROTECTION

God may not always protect you or deliver you the way you expect, but gaining a sense of safety and relaxation is extremely important for recovery. Most of the things you worry about will never happen to you. You need to make a time in your life to gain a sense of protection and safety. Follow the steps in this suggested activity to help you get started.

1. **Put on some soothing music. Pick out one of the suggested psalms and read it out loud. Ask God to be to you what he was to the psalmist.**
2. **Take a deep breath and breathe out slowly. Concentrate on relaxing, and remember that God is a refuge, or focus on the image the psalm gives. Now tighten your toes until your muscles begin to hurt a little and then release your toes. Concentrate on the feeling of letting go, and as you release the tension in your muscles, release your cares to God.**
3. **Continue taking deep, slow breaths. Let yourself relax. Now, begin to tighten up other muscle groups; release each one with a deep breath and concentrate on the feeling of letting go. Go through all the muscle groups in your body.**
4. **This should take about ten to fifteen minutes. Concentrate on the psalm as you rest between muscle groups. Go back to any area that seems tight and tighten that muscle and then let it relax until it loosens up. End this exercise with a prayer for God's protection in your life. Thank him for being there for you.**

## INTERRUPT THE AROUSAL-ACTIVATION CYCLE

1. **Do you feel you have lost control over angry or fearful thoughts? What specific thoughts invade your peace?**

2. **If your mind and heart are invaded by *angry* thoughts, try to interrupt the cycle by saying "Stop!" every time a negative thought or emotion jumps up. After you interrupt the thought, substitute a thought that minimizes the reaction. You can minimize by saying things like, "God is still in control" or "What difference will this make in a**

**hundred years?" Every time the cycle of thoughts and physical arousal starts, interrupt it. Pray instead.**

3. **If your mind and heart are invaded by *fearful* thoughts, try to interrupt the cycle by saying, "Thank you, Lord" every time a fearful thought or emotion jumps up. Finish with the thought that God will be with you. Say aloud a verse you have memorized from one of the psalms. Then do it again every thirty seconds until the thoughts are gone. Practice this response every day for at least six weeks until the alarm reactions subside.**

# 7. The Sabbath Principle of Celebration

## RECOVERY FOCUS

- Make celebration a part of your life.
- Allow celebration to prevent you from taking yourself too seriously.
- Learn to laugh.

## RECOVERY INFORMATION

What is celebration and why is it important for recuperation and rest? Work is often a fight that brings on anxiety, in part because of its focus on problem solving. In contrast, celebration is focused on releasing and having a good time. Celebration also centers on rituals that give honor or validation to people and their efforts.

The sabbaths put an emphasis on festivity and celebration as part of the rest process. The Sabbath of Booths specifically underscores the elements of celebration. This sabbath was a time to enjoy the fruits of the Israelites' labor. Leviticus 23:40–41 speaks of this sabbath: "On the first day you are to take choice fruit from the trees, and palm fronds, leafy branches and poplars, and rejoice before the Lord your God for seven days. Celebrate this as a festival to the Lord for seven days each year." This literally meant that the participants were to be happy for seven days, a difficult task for many.

In Randy Reynolds's early years of ministry, it often seemed that life was all battle and struggle, except for one small ritual that brought tremendous refreshment—a quarterly board meeting with a group of older men. At the meeting, staff members would share the results of their labors, and the board members would praise and encourage the staff. The time of reflecting on the things that God had done strengthened the staff, gave them a change of perspective, and inspired them. In addition, this celebration brought honor to God and the staff.

Celebration allows us the time to enjoy and even experience the fruits of our labor. Without celebration and festivity, life can seem like an endless battle with more losses than victories, and that's a formula for burnout. Randy's father once said, "My life was really pretty good. I just was too busy and tired to realize it." Part of having a sabbath is to stop laboring long enough to allow ourselves to have a good time and realize what blessings we have in our lives.

We often feel that play is for children and that we don't need it. The emphasis in adult life is on responsibility and hard work. However, in accepting these adult responsibilities, we don't have to give up all the pleasures of childhood and become miserable adults. Some Christian groups view fun as sinful, associating it with pagan culture and hedonism. We need to look again at Scripture's view of celebration. We need to affirm once again the freedom to express joy and delight as part of a spiritual experience.

Having the freedom to express spontaneous impulses of playfulness and joy helps us to relax. We can be serious about God and devoted to his kingdom without becoming the "frozen chosen." King David, who was a man after God's own heart, expressed his joy "with all his might" as he danced before the Lord. This playful expression was a part of his culture, and other people joined in by singing, playing musical instruments, and dancing. God created us to gain healing and recovery through these types of experiences.

Ralph came to counseling because he was depressed and had developed a panic disorder. He was in a high-stress job and couldn't afford to make a mistake. His boss gave him a month off work to see if he could stabilize. Ralph had spent every minute of his life in structured, concerted effort, or so it seemed. He was not relaxed, spontaneous, funny, or joyful.

Ralph's doctor put him on medication for the depression and anxiety. Ralph began to do things that were playful and spontaneous, things that enabled him to feel good. He had loved to play tennis as a kid and began to do that again every day. His recovery was amazing. He said in counseling, "I'd become great at working and being successful, but I'd forgotten how to play." Regaining play helped Ralph get back his mental health. The exercise also reduced stress and muscle tension.

## LEARN TO LAUGH

Someone said that the reason the angels fell from heaven is that they took themselves too seriously. We all have a tendency to be too serious about certain things in our lives. Celebration helps us to lighten up and relax. Celebration takes some of the intensity out of life and gives us a freedom from anxiety. God created laughter, which brings healing into our lives. Laughter is usually a part of celebration, a part of having a good time.

A psychologist was treating a woman suffering from panic attacks and agoraphobic reactions (fear of being in an open space). This woman would go into the grocery store, become overwhelmed with fear, and would have to leave because of the intensity of her panic disorder. The psychologist decided to use laughter as a way to break her fear reactions. "The next time you have a panic attack in the supermarket, the next time you are sure you're going to die right then and there," he said, "go over to the fresh fish display and lie down next to it." She was offended by his suggestion and took it as bad advice. A few days later she was shopping and began to feel overwhelmed by fear. She headed straight for the fresh fish. When she got there, she started to lie down, burst into laughter, and couldn't stop laughing as she pictured herself as a dead fish. She was no longer controlled by her fear, and she never again had a panic attack in a grocery store.

Taking life and ourselves too seriously is often the result of a lack of trust in God. When we are relaxed and able to put things in God's hands, we are able to see the humor in difficult situations.

Many of us deal with serious matters that have little room for humor. A few years ago Randy Reynolds was performing a wedding, which ranks second only to funerals when it comes to formality. Randy has always been uncomfortable reading in formal situations, and even though he has performed many weddings, he has never been able to relax.

At this particular wedding, *everything* went wrong: the parents were angry; three hundred people showed up at a church that seated only two hundred seventy; and the wedding started twenty minutes late. The bride and groom were so nervous they were noticeably shaking. As the groom started to put the ring on the bride's finger, she knocked it out of his hand. The ring rolled under her eight-foot train and was lost for several minutes. As the wedding party struggled to regain composure, the bride stopped the service by yelling loudly enough for everyone to hear, "We didn't practice the wedding this way last night!" After the wedding, however, the wedding party was able to laugh. And Randy realized he would never again have to worry at a wedding, because he knew no other wedding could go as badly as this one had.

When we can laugh at ourselves and laugh in difficult situations, it helps relieve stress. A welfare caseworker, whose job was often depressing, collected humorous quotations from application letters to help her get through rough days.

- I am forwarding my marriage certificate and six children. I have had seven, but one died, which was baptized on a half-sheet of paper.
- Mrs. Jones has not had any clothes for a year and has been visited regularly by the clergy.
- I cannot get sick pay. I have six children. Can you tell me why?
- I'm glad to report that my husband who is missing is dead.
- I'm very much annoyed to find that you have branded my son illiterate. This is a dirty lie as I was married a week before he was born.
- My husband got his project cut off two weeks ago, and I haven't had any relief since.
- You have changed my little boy to a girl. Will this make any difference?
- In accordance with your instructions, I have given birth to twins in the enclosed envelope.
- I want my money as quick as I can get it. I have been in bed with doctor two weeks and he doesn't do me good. If things don't improve, I will have to send for another doctor.

Laughter plays an important part in the healing process. Norman Cousins, editor of the *Saturday Review,* contracted a disease that caused him pain. He watched humorous movies and claimed that ten minutes of belly laughter allowed him two hours of pain-free sleep. Laughter stimulates the brain to produce natural pain-relieving chemicals.

God created laughter for a purpose. Only recently have we understood the physiological changes that go on in our bodies when we laugh, changes that bring recovery and healing.

## RECOVERY PROBERS

1. How do you celebrate in your life?

2. What overlooked areas of your life are worth celebrating?

3. Who gives you recognition for your efforts in a positive way?

4. Do you savor the victories that God gives you? How?

5. Create a ritual that would celebrate something meaningful to you or someone close to you. Describe your plan.

6. Name five playful things you did as a child.

7. What is one thing that you know you take too seriously? How can you learn to laugh in this area of your life?

## RECOVERY GUIDE

### Read Ecclesiastes 3:1, 4.

1. How do you take time to laugh as well as to weep, to dance as well as to mourn?

2. What friends can help you find more balance?

### Read Philippians 4:4.

1. What does it mean to rejoice?

2. Do you believe God wants you to enjoy life?

3. What evidence does this verse give to suggest that experiencing full joy is to be an ongoing attitude rather than an occasional experience?

### Read 2 Samuel 6:5.

1. Do you believe that celebration is okay with God?

2. Is it difficult for you to be spontaneous?

### Read Romans 13:7.

1. Part of the meaning of celebration is to take the time to give honor. To whom do you give honor?

**2. Who honors you?**

**3. What makes you feel appreciated?**

## RECOVERY GOALS

**1. Are you willing to bring more times of celebration into your life? What steps will you take to make that happen?**

**2. Rank the degree to which the following elements of celebration are found in your life. Use 1 to signify an element strongly present in your life and 5 to represent an element that is weak or not present in your life.**

- ☐ Laughter
- ☐ Festivity
- ☐ Playfulness and fun
- ☐ Giving and receiving honor
- ☐ Enjoying successes in your life

**3. Make a commitment to practice these elements of celebration in your life during the next month. Plan them into your life rather than just hope they will happen.**

**4. Write out some victories and share them with a friend who would be excited and enthusiastic.**

5. Plan a family night and celebrate family as well as individual successes.

6. Take some money from a paycheck and do something special.

7. Honor someone in your family monthly. Make that person's favorite meal or use a different colored plate at that person's place at the table. Choose a contribution this family member has made and have the other family members say how it affected them or how proud they are of the person. Have a different member plan each time of honor.

8. Practice activities you enjoyed as a child. When you have an impulse to express joy, follow it by saying, "Thank you, Lord," singing a song, giving a hug, jumping up in the air, yelling "yippee," or smiling.

9. Go to a funny movie, read a funny book, find a friend who makes you laugh, collect crazy bumper stickers or funny headlines.

10. Plan a party with all the fun things you can dream up. Or plan a party in which you give recognition to God for his faithfulness in your life; sing songs and have everyone bring some instrument that makes noise.

# 8. The Sabbath Principle of Quiet Reflection

## RECOVERY FOCUS

- Learn to value quiet reflection.
- Use reflection to focus on priorities and balanced perspective.
- Set limits to protect your priorities.

## RECOVERY INFORMATION

The Sabbath is a time to be still, to spend special time with God. As Psalm 46:10 says, "Be still, and know that I am God." The Sabbath is not only a time of celebrating and finding safety but also a time of reflection and inspiration as our spirits are touched by God.

When people think of disengaging from work, they often think of recreation rather than reflection. While recreation and entertainment help distract or disengage us, they don't necessarily do anything to make us better people. They provide escape but no inspiration.

Reflection and inspiration help us to see ourselves and give us wisdom, strength, and courage from God. Reflection helps us go beyond our natural self and become more Christlike. Inspiration empowers us to do well in our life tasks. Inspiration puts us in touch with the enduring values and meaning of life.

Reflection also helps us see when we are being externally controlled and driven. It frees us to be motivated internally and to be able to rest in the Lord. We often are able to plan our lives and take charge more effectively in quiet, solitary times rather than during periods when we are pushed and pulled by many demands and crises. The clarity of direction that comes from stillness helps us to invest ourselves in meaningful activity. It protects us from burnout and relapse.

David, in Psalm 139:23–24, says, "Search me, O God, and know my heart; test me and know my anxious thoughts. See if there is any offensive way in me, and lead me in the way everlasting." As David got in touch with God, he also got in touch with himself, his thoughts, his feelings, and his behaviors.

You can bring renewal into your life by listening to God and letting go of your concerns and striving. Do you keep a journal that helps you to be in touch with your feelings? Do you have a regular time of planning and evaluation to see if you are staying true to your values and priorities? Are you growing in character, becoming faithful, merciful, just, loving—the qualities that make you more like Christ?

Many great men and women practiced taking time out of their busy schedules to reflect. Martin Luther, who started the Reformation in the 1500s, would take additional time to pray in the morning if he knew he had an exceptionally busy day. John Wesley, who was instrumental in bringing about revival in England in the 1700s, spent up to several hours every morning to prepare for doing God's will that day. Aleksandr Solzhenitsyn, who received the Nobel prize for literature in 1970, spoke of his time in the Russian prisons. He said the solitude helped him reflect, enabling him to see himself more clearly and to exercise his creativity. Fred Smith, a Christian businessman, described his former boss, who found inspiration and strength from reading five chapters of Scripture a day as well as biographies of men and women of strong character. These readings gave his boss courage and motivation as he moved Genesco from a company of seventy-five employees to one of seventy-five thousand employees over the years!

We all need to be challenged, no matter what our background or present work setting. We need input that gives us courage to overcome the difficulties we experience. What inspires you? What books, people, experiences, or activities motivate you in your life? What gives you courage to overcome difficulty and strength to endure hard times? What challenges you to live a better life?

When you face stressful situations, take time for a sabbath of reflection. Step back from your circumstances and ask the bigger questions. Read the Bible and other helpful books to regain a balanced perspective. Talk out your situation with a trusted, godly friend.

Reflection in the midst of hard times can bring definition and clarity. Reflection can be the sandpaper that smooths out the rough edges of our circumstances, allowing us to see the shape and meaning of what is going on. Sometimes reflection brings a dramatic revelation that slaps us in the face. Other times we experience a gradual calm that brings serenity.

In her book *Making Sunday Special,* Karen Mains describes the traditional Jewish Sabbath observance. One of the first activities is the lighting of two candles: one symbolizing the word *observe* and one symbolizing the word *remember.* Those are significant images for the rest that comes from quiet reflection. When we observe the sabbath and remember and rehearse God's goodness in the past, we gain inner strength and peace.

## SETTING LIMITS

One of God's purposes in creating the sabbaths was to set limits on his people. The sabbath was a boundary that God set so his people would not overextend themselves. Reflection helps us gain a clearer perspective, reestablish our priorities, and set boundaries. We need to define what is important to us and mark off that territory. When those boundaries are crossed, we then can know that something is amiss in our lives.

Years ago Randy Reynolds and his two young children visited his grandmother in a nursing home. The children were bored after forty-five minutes and began to whine and cry. After wrestling with their whining for twenty minutes, he reached the end of his patience. He picked up his son and headed down the hallway. He felt angry and hassled and would have traded his son at the moment for a well-behaved dog or cat.

His struggles with the children had squeezed his perspective of fathering into a burden rather than a blessing. As Randy and his son walked down the hall, an old man approached them. The man looked Randy in the face and said with envy, "Is he yours?" Randy was about to say, "Yes, but you can have him if you want," when Randy's daughter came running down the hall. When the man saw her, he turned back to Randy and with a voice full of joy and wonder asked, "Is she yours also?" As Randy nodded yes, embarrassed for the way he had been feeling, the old man said, "Well, you are a rich man, truly a rich man."

The struggles and hassles of everyday life can cause us to lose sight of what is valuable. We must take time to be still and regain the perspective that makes our lives worth fighting for.

One of the mistakes Randy made in the nursing home was that he didn't respect his children's limits. Because of that disrespect, both he and they were pushed over their limits. Often, one of the main factors in dealing with stress and burnout is whether people are willing to respect their own limits and set some boundaries for themselves.

God wants us to respect our limits and make provision for those limits. Having a time of quiet reflection can show us where we are not protecting ourselves and setting limits. The following are some mistaken beliefs that keep us from respecting our limits. Check the ones that apply to you:

- ☐ I don't have any limits.
- ☐ I feel responsible, and if I don't keep at my work, I know it won't get done.
- ☐ I'm being selfish and ungodly if I think of myself.
- ☐ My needs and limits don't count; only my work and other people count.
- ☐ Other people will be angry and reject me if I set limits, and I won't be able to handle that.
- ☐ I can do things better than other people can, so I have to do everything.
- ☐ If I don't accept every challenge, I will not be important.

List other beliefs that keep you from maintaining healthy limits.

- 
- 
- 
- 

We need to replace our mistaken beliefs with healthy ones, ones that bring us sabbath rest, ones that keep us from overextending ourselves. Read over the following list of healthy beliefs. Place a + in the box of beliefs you already have incorporated into your life; place a √ in the box of beliefs you want to incorporate into your life.

- ☐ I have limits, and I respect them.
- ☐ God is ultimately responsible in life, and I will see the best results if I respect my limits and trust God with my tasks.
- ☐ Taking care of myself is my God-given responsibility. God values me and cares about my limits and needs, so I also need to care.

- ☐ I will not die if others are angry or disappointed with me. It's more important to please God and pay attention to my values and priorities than to give in to others' disapproval.
- ☐ It's important to delegate responsibilities to others. They can be helpful if I will be patient with them.
- ☐ I'm important to God and myself because of who I am, not because of what I do.

## RECOVERY PROBERS

**1. Do you make time to be by yourself to reflect on God and your life? When?**

**2. What gives you the most meaning in your life today?**

**3. Do you spend most of your time doing meaningful activities or activities that are unrelated to your core values or priorities? Explain.**

**4. What do you feel you could not live without?**

**5. What distracts you from those things that are meaningful? How can you stay more on track with who you are and what your values are?**

6. **What are the blind spots that bring you down when you become too busy to be in touch with God or yourself? (Example: I become driven under pressure. I get angry and hurt others. I worry and exaggerate my problems.)**

7. **What inspires you to be more Christlike?**

## RECOVERY GUIDE

The quiet time of reflection is very important in helping us receive the spiritual nurturing that can sustain us and move us forward in our lives. Reflecting on Scripture will inspire, give direction, and give courage. In some biblical stories we find how people learned to set limits and delegate responsibilities. We also find passages that produce endurance and renewal.

### Read Joshua 1:5–9.

1. **On what did Joshua's prosperity and success depend?**

2. **What was the prerequisite for doing God's "law" (v. 8)?**

3. **On what do you meditate when you need courage and strength to accomplish your daily tasks?**

4. **Is that promise also for you? How does that strengthen you?**

**Read Exodus 18:17–23.**

1. **Was Moses' work important?**

2. **What was Moses' father-in-law's concern?**

3. **Was this a godly concern? Why?**

4. **What practical advice did the father-in-law give?**

5. **Is it difficult for you to allow others to relieve you of responsibilities? Why?**

6. **In what areas of your life do you need to delegate responsibility?**

7. **To whom can you delegate?**

**Read Isaiah 40:28–31.**

**1. What is God's promise for stressed-out people?**

**2. How does God fill and renew you when you are feeling weary and tired?**

**3. How can you "hope in the Lord," especially in your burn-out areas?**

## RECOVERY GOALS

Make a commitment to have some solitary time when you can reflect on your life and relationship with God.

**1. Make a list of your top priorities.**

2. Examine each priority and rate it from 1–3. A 3 means you rarely live according to this priority. A 2 means you sometimes live with this priority in mind. A 1 means you are daily aware that this priority shapes your life.

3. What do your list and your rating tell you about your life?

4. What changes do you need to make?

5. Make a list of books that will help you reflect on your relationship to God and inspire you to live more effectively.

6. What people or experiences inspire you toward growth in your values and priorities?

7. Do you need to build into your life more time for these people and experiences? How will you do that?

**8. What is most draining in your life?**

**9. How can you set a limit or boundary to protect yourself?**

**10. What is stopping you from setting these limits?**

**11. Where do you fail to plan in your life?**

# 9. The Sabbath Principle of Hope and Restoration

## RECOVERY FOCUS

- Learn the sabbath principle of hope and restoration.
- Trust God to give you hope in times of loss.
- Choose the way of hope.

## RECOVERY INFORMATION

Much of the stress we experience is the result of *losses*—loss of control, loss of financial freedom, loss of emotional stability, loss of productivity, loss of relationships, loss of dreams, to name a few. When we face losses, we are in danger of losing one of most important ingredients of our serenity and peace: *hope*. And when we lose hope, we are in danger of relapsing into destructive behavior patterns.

Looking at two of the Old Testament sabbaths may help us understand how God provides hope for us and restores us in times of loss. Leviticus 25 describes two important sabbaths God structured into the Israelite culture: the Sabbatical Year and the Year of Jubilee.

The Sabbatical Year was to be celebrated every seven years. The Israelites were to work their fields for six years, but during the seventh, they were to allow the land to rest (Leviticus 25:1–7). The Lord promised his people that during the sixth year of planting, the land would provide three years' worth of food. But the people had to trust that God would keep this promise (Leviticus 25:18–22). God built into the culture a year that people would look forward to—a year of hope, a year of rest and celebration.

The Year of Jubilee was to be celebrated every fifty years (or after every seven Sabbatical Years). It was a time of hope, forgiveness, and a new start. Jews in debt were to be released from what they owed. Anyone imprisoned in debtors' jail was to be released. Any slaves were to be set free. All land was returned to its original owners (Leviticus 25:8–17).

Now, we will quickly acknowledge that these two sabbaths do not have a direct correlation to specific aspects of our culture. Your boss most likely has not announced that since the company made good profits for the past six years, you may have a year off with full benefits. And the bank most likely has not called to announce that your mortgage has just been paid off.

But we can draw some principles from these two sabbaths. It's significant that these sabbaths began on the Day of Atonement, the day God set aside for the atonement of Israel's sins, after which the nation was again in right standing with God. The message was this: sin brought burdens but God's sabbaths brought forgiveness, hope, and restoration.

Many of the Israelites' burdens and stresses were dealt with in these two sabbaths. Both brought personal relief and restoration. Both demonstrated to the Jews that they owned nothing; everything belonged to God.

The sabbaths gave them hope in the face of their losses. The sabbaths restored to them their sense of security, their land, their freedom from debt and slavery, their relationship to God. It helped the Israelites to believe that their mistakes were covered and that someday there would be good things in their lives, rather than just difficulty and loss.

We need the hope that restores our weary spirits. "Hope is both the earliest and most indispensable virtue inherent in the state of being alive. . . . If life is to be sustained, hope must remain even where confidence is wounded, trust impaired," said Albert Schweitzer in *Civilization and Ethics*. The worship of God during the sabbath was to remind believers that God is a sustainer of life and that he gives hope in life.

## COPING WITH LOSSES

We all deal with losses differently. Let's look at three people who faced losses. Note how hope or lack of it played a part in the person's ability to find restoration.

Jim, a recovering alcoholic, had been sober for five years. He was married for the second time, had started a family, and was excited about his first son. Jim had done well staying sober, but he had not done too well in maintaining his serenity. Jim was a hard worker and was often upset over the difficulties at work. He would bring that anger home and yell at Laura, his wife. She would get upset and become distant and less affectionate. Jim responded by becoming angrier.

Within six months Laura left Jim. He was devastated. He tried everything to get her back, but nothing worked. As he began to lose hope in the relationship, he began to lose hope in life. He said, "I just don't care any more. I don't have anything to live for."

With his loss of hope, Jim had a relapse and began drinking again. He was caught drinking and driving with the baby in the car and subsequently lost custody rights. Jim had to start all over again in regaining sobriety because he had lost hope in life.

Are you like Jim? Have you lost your hope? Have you found yourself relapsing into destructive behavior patterns? Clinging to hope, to the sabbath promises of forgiveness and restoration, can make all the difference.

Jamie was another story. Jamie had been in various types of ministry for fifteen years. Most of these ministries involved working with students, street people, and inner-city kids. None of the jobs paid very much.

When Jamie's church cut the funding for a program to develop a youth ministry, Jamie decided to finish his degree in social work. But that would not be easy. He was now in his late thirties, with a wife and two children to support. He and his family struggled financially as he worked to get the credits he needed to graduate.

In the last semester before graduation, Jamie realized they would soon be out of money. He decided that he must quit school and go back to work if he could not find a way to finance his last few months of schooling. He was discouraged about the loss of financial security, but he maintained his hope in God. He trusted that God would provide, even if that meant he needed to drop out of his degree program.

Shortly after this realization, Jamie received a phone call. The person calling asked Jamie if he was sitting down. When Jamie asked the caller to identify himself, the voice said, "You have won the Publishers Clearing House sweepstakes!" Jamie couldn't believe it. Suddenly he was financially secure. He now had the freedom to minister to people in need without worrying about his personal finances.

Most stories of hope in a time of loss do not end this dramatically.

But the point is this: No matter what we lose, the Christian can afford to hope in God, the God who provides, the God who leads us to rest, the God who restores us.

By the time Bob was forty-two, he had achieved a significant position with a large company. However, when the company faced extensive cutbacks, he was left without a job. Bob grieved his losses and went through a time of hopelessness. He became depressed.

Bob began to read the Bible, asking God to show him what he was to do with the rest of his life. Over time, God helped Bob understand himself, and Bob regained his sense of hope.

He decided that he would rather work for himself, but he realized that the cost to himself and his family would be high. He knew he was good in his field. He had never had the courage or the motivation to go out on his own before, but now found himself free to work toward his dream of being a consultant. He soon saw his loss as an opportunity given by God to achieve a dream. He worked hard and came up with new ideas and ways to market them. Within three years he was earning in three days what it took him six days to earn at his old company. Bob's hope had become a reality through trust in God, desire, risk, creativity, and hard work.

## LEARNING TO HOPE

When you face a loss, you have a choice: will you lose hope and relapse into unhealthy behaviors that sabotage the hope of rebuilding or will you grieve your losses, hope in God, and allow him to restore you?

Hope is a choice. Christians can choose to hope because God has shown himself to be worthy of our trust and hope. The God of the sabbaths says to us in our losses, "Take heart. Don't lose hope. Trust me to provide for you and direct you. I will restore you so that you can have a fresh start."

The hopeful person is marked by several characteristics. Read over the following list and rate yourself on a scale from 1 to 10, with 10 representing a characteristic that is strongly present in your life.

- ☐ You have a knowledge of your own strengths and weaknesses.
- ☐ You are able to gain self-esteem from many sources and are able to change those sources, gleaning self-worth from God, family, career, friends, personality, appearance, and gifts.

- ☐ You have a willingness to tolerate change and distress.
- ☐ You have courage in the face of threat.
- ☐ You are able to disengage emotionally and rest in God.
- ☐ Your trust in God helps you look for the good in life.
- ☐ You take charge and work toward making life good.
- ☐ You have a strong will to live; you don't deny problems but fight through them.
- ☐ You are realistic in your thinking. You look at your environment and appraise it reasonably, but you also include God in your appraisal.
- ☐ You have a sense of humor about your life.

## RECOVERY PROBERS

**1. When you get discouraged and lose hope, where do you go to regain hope? Is hope found in what you can see and feel?**

**2. Do you have realistic expectations in your life?**

**3. Do you lose hope because life is not the way it "should be"? Give an example.**

**4. When you begin to gain hope, do you become too dependent on results and get discouraged when things don't go the way you expect them to? Example: A person who starts a new business expects it to go well and becomes discouraged every time there is a bad day. The discouragement leads to behavior that sabotages the success of the business.**

5. **Do you have a difficult time surrendering your expectations to God and continuing to work and persevere toward a positive end? Explain.**

6. **In what ways do you look for God to take the difficult things in your life and bring good things from them?**

7. **Describe a situation when something bad happened and something good came out of that bad situation. Share the story with your group or a friend.**

8. **When you rest and gather new ideas, do you gain a sense of well-being and hope? Give an example.**

9. **Are you aware of any unresolved guilt that could be undermining your hope? What will you do with that guilt?**

## RECOVERY GUIDE

Hope can be both passive and active. It can be anchored in unrealistic wishes or realistic expectations, temporary things or eternal things. The fact is that we need hope. We need to have expectations that life can offer good and meaningful things to us. Without hope, life loses its color, its ability to arouse and engage us. Imagine the hope that the Year of Jubilee offered the slaves, who could look forward to being freed and owning land again.

**Read Proverbs 13:12.**

1. **What hopes have been deferred in your life?**

2. **How have you responded to those deferred hopes?**

3. **Does God want us to believe that we will have good things in this life?**

4. **Do you have something you look forward to every day? What is it?**

**Read Psalm 27:13–14.**

1. **What does it mean to wait for the Lord?**

2. **In what ways is waiting for the Lord like hoping in God?**

**Read Romans 5:1–5.**

1. **How does hope in eternal things anchor your soul?**

2. **How do you invest in eternal things?**

3. **What does "growing in character" mean to you?**

## RECOVERY GOALS

How do you gain hope when you have lost it? When a person feels stuck, hopeless, and helpless, how can hope be revived? Webster describes hope as, "a feeling that what is wanted will happen." Many exhausted people have given up hope. In other words they have let go of their personal desires.

Stimulation of ideas is an important part of blowing on the dying coals of a person's hopes. Having conversations with others, reading books, or writing can stimulate hope. Hearing a story about people struggling with similar problems and seeing how they have overcome their challenges can inspire hope. Being around hopeful people is often encouraging and stimulating.

1. **In what areas have you given up hope? Are you willing to regain your sense of hope?**

2. **What are you doing to produce hope in your life?**

**3. What can you specifically do to ease your burdens and give yourself more hope?**

**4. When will you be willing to do this?**

**5. What area of your life needs rebuilding?**

**6. What will you do to begin the rebuilding?**

**7. What one thing will you build into your life to look forward to on a daily basis?**

# 10. Overcoming Burnout from Resentment

## RECOVERY FOCUS

- Recognize burnout that results from resentment.
- Find freedom from inner "oughts" and "shoulds."
- Find the freedom offered by the sabbath principle.

## RECOVERY INFORMATION

"I seem to vacillate between depression or apathy and a slow-burning resentment," said John, a man in his midforties. "I work hard. Then I come home and do the maintenance things around the house. I enjoy all that stuff; it's what I'm good at. But I feel empty inside. I get angry at my wife because she doesn't seem interested in me. I really don't even care about sex that much any more, but I resent it that she has so little interest. I love my kids, but I often feel irritable and resentful that they are so demanding. At times I don't know why I'm doing everything that I do. I suppose I just have to, not that I don't want to. . . ." His voice faded away.

To John, life was feeling unfair, a common cause of stress and burnout. He felt he was giving to others but little was coming back his way, and he resented it. He felt unable to make any changes because he loved his family and needed his job. He saw no options.

When John's counselor confronted him about change, John said, "I'm a very responsible person, and I'd feel guilty if I didn't do everything I'm doing." Through counseling, John began to see that he was a compulsive person and because of that, he covered up or ignored many of his feelings. He did things out of duty, "shoulds," and "oughts," and was motivated by guilt and fear. He was controlled by responsibilities and others' expectations. He didn't have much inner freedom. He was a driven man, and his spirit showed it.

John lacked serenity. He felt he couldn't say no to the "shoulds" in his life. Because of this, he had a very difficult time getting rest and renewal.

Was John's sense of responsibility wrong? Isn't responsibility part of a Christian's response to life? Yes. In fact, doing what's right is also a part of God's sabbath. In Isaiah 58, the Lord says that healing and restoration come by keeping the sabbath, by doing right and good things.

Recent studies confirm that people who do good deeds receive health benefits. Hans Selye, a researcher in the area of stress, believes that when we help others, our bodies release endorphins, natural pain-killing chemicals that give us an overall sense of well-being. This sense of well-being protects us from the effects of stress. Several studies have also shown that when we are involved in good deeds, our bodies release secretions that improve our immune systems.

John's problem was not that he was doing good and right things but that he was *compulsive* about it. He was controlled by external pressures and insecurities. He was doing responsible things but resenting life and others. John's type-A personality (driven and often angry) could cause him health problems if he doesn't deal with his resentment.

The sabbath principle speaks to this issue. When God ordained the Old Testament sabbaths, he created them to provide rest, renewal, and restoration. But several centuries later, the religious leaders had taken this positive, life-giving sabbath gift and had turned it into an enormous burden. They were obsessed with "shoulds" and "oughts" and drained all life from the meaning of the sabbaths. The people began to resent the sabbath as a complicated chore rather than as an observance that would bring inner freedom to their lives.

God made it clear that the sabbaths were created for our benefit. The sabbaths were to be a time when people would find inner wholeness—when their inner life, their values, feelings, and desires would be more consistent with their behaviors. The sabbaths were to be times to take care of some of our needs.

Driven people do not grow up because they feel controlled by "shoulds" and pressures, and they have a difficult time taking care of themselves. They overlook their own needs for rest, nutrition, space, and nurture.

Are you like John? Do you see the sabbaths as something for somebody else? Are you able to take sabbaths and take care of yourself?

Part of John's problem with resentment and burnout was that he expected others to take care of him. After all, he gave so much to others, he felt it was not fair that others didn't give as much to him. He felt entitled to his resentment. He felt others owed him love and appreciation because he did so much for them. He obligated them to himself by his contributions to them, whether they wanted that obligation or not. He then felt resentment when they didn't do what he wanted them to do. He put a guilt trip on others and played the martyr. Other times he would feel disappointed and depressed that others were not more sensitive to him. When he felt like this, he would just mope around the house.

As John began to grow, he defined what he valued in his life and what he wanted to do. He decided that certain tasks pleased God and that certain attitudes didn't please God. He decided to adopt the attitudes that pleased God. When he did this, he felt better about himself and his relationship with God. John's self-esteem improved. He had more inner freedom and was less driven.

John realized, for instance, that the Bible study he attended was not a healthy thing for him. He had a difficult time relating to the leader and went to the study only to please his wife. John decided that he was no longer obligated to attend that study and quit going. Instead, he began teaching a Sunday school class in which his son was involved, and he found he really enjoyed that. When John gained the freedom to say no to some of his drivenness, he also gained a clearer perspective of his values and was able to live more consistently with them.

John's burnout had been fueled by his resentments. John lacked an inner satisfaction and joy. He often found his motivation in life was too dependent on the responses of others. As John became free of this dependency, he found something paradoxical happening. As he was free to love without being demanding, others loved him more. It now seemed as if he needed others' approval less and received it more. He also found himself free to ask for what he wanted and to define his expectations.

His growth in this area resulted in part because now that he gave himself permission to say no, he could also accept other people saying no to him. He could communicate with less stress. John was more comfortable with others' disapproval when he said no because he felt God had given him permission to be who he is rather than who others thought he should be. He had some boundaries that protected him from external demands and allowed him some rest and renewal. John was practicing some of the sabbath principles and finding an inner freedom.

## RECOVERY PROBERS

1. What "shoulds" and "oughts" drive you?

2. How does trusting God and God's grace give you freedom from your compulsions?

3. What do you do to stop the begrudging feelings?

4. In what ways can the sabbath principle help you find freedom from this deadening sense of obligation?

5. In what ways do you obligate other people to you and expect them to know what their obligations to you are?

6. How does your relationship with God help your outer life line up with your inner life?

**7. Are you able to define your expectations with others and live within those expectations without resentment?**

**8. Describe an experience where you were able to communicate your thoughts, feelings, and desires in a relationship.**

## RECOVERY GUIDE

Scripture makes it clear that we don't need to feel driven by being good or perfect to gain God's approval. It also says that we will never make life right by our own efforts and that ultimately God is in control. However, in almost the same breath, it emphasizes the importance of good deeds.

**Read Ephesians 2:8–10.**

**1. How is working for approval different from doing good deeds because of who you are and what you do?**

**2. How are we freed from compulsiveness when we become more secure with who we are and when we are able to trust God more?**

**Read Isaiah 58:6–9.**

**1. How do you feel when you do right and just things in your life?**

2. What happens in your heart when you see someone in need provided for?

Read Galatians 5:1, 13.

1. When is it necessary to resist pressures in order to be free?

2. Where does the pressure come from in your life?

3. How does having freedom allow you to love others better?

## RECOVERY GOALS

1. What percentage of your life is driven by "shoulds"?

2. What percentage is motivated by healthy "want to's"?

3. Are you living out your beliefs, standards, and values? Explain.

4. How does your inner life line up with your outer life?

**5. How can the sabbath principles help you find freedom?**

**6. What are you willing to do to change (examples: face yourself and your drivenness; say no to others and set realistic limits; define your expectations of others; let go of hidden resentments; define and integrate your values into your behavior)?**

**7. When will you be willing to do these things?**

**8. How are you going to do these things?**

**9. What would keep you from following through on these ideas? Turn that over to God and make a commitment to do it.**

# LEADER'S GUIDE

## WORKING WITH STRESSED PEOPLE

Leaders of this kind of group will do best if they are more impressed by balance than by hard work or productivity. Often, people who are burnt out are overfunctioners who are trying hard to be good or responsible. They may be great at achieving, but poor at just being or enjoying. Effective leaders will validate group members for their *being,* not their *doing*. If the group can learn to give positive feedback for rest and being, the members will achieve wholeness and recovery.

## PURPOSE OF GROUP

Involve people in defining this purpose so that they have some personal ownership in the group dynamic and can define some of their personal goals.

1. To bring people relief from their drivenness
2. To give information about stress
3. To encourage people not to value their work more than they value God, themselves, and other people
4. To help stressed people gain balance in their lives
5. To provide practical steps for healing

## GROUP FORMAT

Suggested size of group: 8–12 members.

Suggested length of time for the group: 12–15 weeks, spending 1–2 hours per session.

### Opening Sessions

1. Define the purposes of the group and ask why people are there.
2. Read together the Group Ground Rules, found on the following pages.
3. Ask each person to take 10–15 minutes to give his or her personal background and tell his or her story.
4. Define your expectations of attendance and workbook involvement. Get clear commitments from group members.
5. Establish a support network for the group members. Talk

about meeting outside the group for coffee, exchange phone numbers, and the like.

### Workbook Sessions

1. Open each session with prayer, asking for God's presence to protect and lead the group.
2. Share victories, especially those related to previous chapters. Encourage people to share goals they have met.
3. Discuss the various sections of the week's workbook chapter, asking questions about the Recovery Information and using the questions in the Recovery Probers and Recovery Guide for group discussion.
4. Share current struggles. Allow people time to work on struggles.
5. Pray together each week.

### Closing Sessions

1. Focus on what has been gained by reflecting on victories.
2. Talk about what relationships have been meaningful.
3. Make a commitment to have a reunion in three months.
4. Talk about where people can now find support.

## GROUP GROUND RULES

1. All conversations in this group are confidential and may not be shared with anyone outside the group. If permission is asked and everyone is comfortable, an exception can be made. Protection leading to trust building is a goal of this group.
2. These groups aren't open groups, which means that others can't be invited after the group starts. There can be exceptions if the group and the group leader agree.
3. It is important that people share what they are experiencing and that they don't generalize. They need to own their own feelings and not judge others. For example, "I'm tired of the demands my boss makes on me" rather than "Employers expect too much from us."
4. Members aren't responsible for other members; group members are not responsible to give advice, excuse other people's actions, or fix hurting people. What this means is there is no cross-talk allowed. Group members may share experiences from their point of view if someone in the group

needs that information. This group will have a tendency to validate others for their achievements and discount the value of rest and care. The leader will need to redirect group members if this becomes an issue.

5. Listen without interrupting, unless you are the leader and responsible to watch the time in sharing. Each person's story and experience is valuable. Each group member is valuable.
6. Avoid using "shoulds" or "oughts" in the group, either for yourself or others.
7. If a group member becomes anxious about the group experience, talk about it in the group. If a group member wants to quit the group over fearful feelings or resentment, talk about it in the group. Do a reality check with the person, helping him or her to see if the fear is warranted or just a part of the recovery process. Honesty is a key to successful recovery. And honesty can be practiced at times like this in the group.
8. Stay on the goals and purposes of the group and keep conversations directed.
9. Make and express additional ground rules that would make this group a more effective place for recovery to occur.
10. Avoid quick recovery without lifestyle change. For example: "I feel much better. I can get back to work now." Recovery usually stops when this occurs.

## GROUP PROCESS

Groups form in stages. The initial stage is bonding, a stage in which group members share about themselves and find out if the group is safe. The leader's role is to facilitate safety and openness. Leaders need to work toward giving everyone the opportunity to share. Be careful not to allow group members to try to rescue each other.

In later stages, the group members will jockey for positions. Don't be surprised if group members challenge your leadership and some members re-create in the group the dysfunctional behavior that made them stressed out in the first place. Your role is to avoid thinking like a victim or rescuer and to move the group and its members toward personal responsibility, godliness, and healthy thinking. This gives opportunity for real dialogue between group members and for teaching of new life-management skills.

In the last stages, the group needs to learn to let go and say good-by in a healthy way. Help the group to focus on what they have learned and how they have grown. Help group members reflect on their victories and express their joy from lifestyle changes. Your role will be one of helping members not to rationalize but to face their feelings, have fun, and make lifestyle changes.

## REFERRALS

People who are overly stressed often experience depression, grief, and high levels of anxiety. Any signs of deep depression such as insomnia, significant weight loss or weight gain, withdrawal from life tasks, or suicidal thoughts signal problems that are too serious to be handled in a support group. Refer people with these signs to a pastor, counseling professional, or hospital. Other issues may arise that would call for referrals. When developing a referral list, consider:

1. Caring churches that minister to people
2. Treatment centers
3. Christian counselors
4. Social service agencies

## SUGGESTED QUALIFICATIONS FOR GROUP LEADERS

For maximum effectiveness, leaders will have

1. actively practiced the biblical principles of sabbath recovery in their personal lives.
2. been a Christian for several years and have a basic knowledge of the Bible.
3. a dynamic relationship with Christ and a commitment to pray daily for their group members.
4. experience in facilitating a group. If possible, leaders will first serve as co-leaders of a group before having primary leadership responsibilities.
5. experience teaching and practicing basic communication skills, like "using 'I messages,'" "reflective listening," "problem ownership," "making requests" and the like.
6. accountability to the leaders of the facility in which the support group meets. For instance, if the group meets in a church and is sanctioned by the church, support-group leaders will be accountable to the church's leadership.
7. wisdom on knowing when to refer group members for professional help.

8. Christ-centered motives for leading a group.
9. no anxiety about strong expressions of emotion.
10. demonstrated diligence in working through his or her own issues with stress.

# SUGGESTED READINGS

If you found this Recovery Discovery workbook helpful, you may also find help from the following books:

Campolo, Tony. *The Success Fantasy.* Wheaton, Ill.: Victor Books, 1989.

Engram, Ric. *Pace Yourself: Daily Devotions for Those Who Do Too Much.* Nashville: Nelson, 1991.

Hansel, Tim. *When I Feel Guilty.* Elgin, Ill.: David C. Cook, 1979.

Swindoll, Charles. *Stress Fractures: Biblical Splints for Everyday Pressures.* Portland, Oregon: Multnomah, 1991.

Smith, Ken. *It's About Time.* Wheaton, Ill.: Crossway, 1992.

Sprinkle, Patricia. *Women Who Do Too Much: Stress and the Myth of the Superwoman.* Grand Rapids: Zondervan, 1991.

Van Vonderen, Jess. *Tired of Trying to Measure Up.* Minneapolis: Bethany, 1989.

West, Sheila. *Beyond Chaos: Stress Relief for the Working Woman.* Colorado Springs: NavPress, 1991.